Dora Nash is a Cambridge graduate and mother of four who has been involved in preparing young teenagers for Confirmation in several parishes over twenty years, and has been Head of RE and Senior Tutor at The Oratory School, Woodcote, Reading.

Confirmed in the Faith

Grateful thanks are due to my colleagues at
The Oratory School for piloting this material.

NIHIL OBSTAT   Monsignor Canon G. Chidgey, Prot. Ap., J.C.D.
                  CENSOR

IMPRIMATUR   Most Rev. Peter Smith, LL.B., J.C.D
                  Archbishop of Cardiff

17th June, 2003

The *Nihil Obstat* and *Imprimatur* are official declarations that a book or pamphlet is free from doctrinal error. No implication is contained therein that those who have granted the *Nihil Obstat* and *Imprimatur* necessarily recommend or endorse the book or pamphlet.

Confirmed in the Faith

A Catholic Confirmation Course

Dora Nash

GRACEWING

First published in 2003
Reprinted 2007, 2009, 2012
New revised edition 2016

Gracewing
2 Southern Avenue, Leominster
Herefordshire HR6 0QF

All rights reserved. No part of this publication may be reproduced, stored in a
retrieval system, or transmitted in any form, or by any means, electronic,
mechanical, photocopying, recording or otherwise, without the written permission
of the publisher.

Text © Dora Nash 2003, 2016
Illustrations © Saint Michael's Abbey Press, Farnborough

None of the illustrations from this book may be reproduced without written
permission from the Prior of St Michael's Abbey

The right of Dora Nash to be identified as the author of this work has been asserted
in accordance with the Copyright, Designs and Patents Act, 1988

ISBN 978 085244 545 7

Typesetting by Action Publishing Technology Ltd,
Gloucester, GL1 5SR

Contents

Confirmed in the Faith

To the candidate

You are approaching Confirmation. Over the following weeks you will be preparing to receive this sacrament by following this course. Bring this booklet to each session. The only other thing you will need is something to write with and, most importantly, a **Bible**.

Before you start the course, you might be asking yourself some of these questions:

What is Confirmation?
It is the Sacrament in which Jesus seals you with the Holy Spirit. You are joined more closely to Jesus and become a full member of his Church.

Why do I need to be Confirmed?
To complete your Baptism which you received as a baby. Now the Holy Spirit will help you to become more fully mature in Christ.

Why am I Confirmed at this age?
The age that Confirmation is given can vary. It's mostly given in the early teen years to show you that you are now becoming an adult member of the Church.

What will this Confirmation course be about?
It will be about Our Lord Jesus Christ and how his life fills our lives. It will aim to give you a more adult understanding of the Faith in which you are going to be confirmed. It will help you to see what being sealed by the Holy Spirit really means.

Session One

Our Lord Jesus Christ –

A Personal Commitment

What can the world offer you without Jesus?
Whoever finds Jesus, finds a rich treasure,
and a good above every good.

From *The Imitation of Christ* by Thomas A Kempis

PER·IPSVM

ET·CVM·IPSO·ET·IN·IPSO

EST·TIBI

OMNIS·HONOR·ET·GLORIA

Our Lord Jesus Christ – A Personal Commitment

When we are confirmed we take a great step towards Jesus Christ. To show that we want to love and serve him, we

- ask to be full members of his family, the Church

- make again the promises that were made for us when we were baptised

- offer ourselves to be apostles for him in the world.

And in return, he fills us with his Spirit and with his life, giving us the gifts and the strength to do his will.

It is a great Sacrament.

Our starting point must be Jesus himself. We need to get to know him better and to love him more, so that we can take that great step and be worthy to receive what he gives.

How well do I know him? What does he mean to me?

'Who do you say that I am?'

One day during his journeys around Israel with his chosen apostles, Jesus asked them this question: 'Who do people say that I am?' They replied that the people of the time thought he was John the Baptist or one of the old prophets come back to life. 'But you,' he said, 'who do you say that I am?'

For Discussion
Who do people today think Jesus is? What do you think
* – a great man sent by God like Moses?*
– the founder of a religion, like Mohammed?
– a famous person in history?
– a social reformer? a revolution-ary? a do-gooder?
– a saint? a wise preacher?
– any other kind of person?

Finding out about Jesus

We find out about Jesus and his life and teaching from the four gospels. Here in St Luke's Gospel, at the beginning of his public life, we see Jesus claiming to be the special person whom God had promised to send to save and help.

Jesus stood up to read in the synagogue and they handed him the scroll of the prophet Isaiah. Unrolling the scroll he found the place where it is written:
The Spirit of the Lord has been given to me for he has anointed me.
He has sent me to bring the good news to the poor,
to proclaim liberty to captives and to the blind new sight,
to set the downtrodden free,
to proclaim the Lord's year of favour.
Then he began to speak to them, 'This text is being fulfilled today even as you listen'.

(Luke 4:16–21)

Many times in the Gospels, Jesus gave hints and signs to his followers about who he really was, especially when he worked miracles. In some miracles he really did give the blind new sight; in others he raised people from death, or showed his power over nature.

Here is an account of Jesus'

miracle in a fisherman's boat on the Sea of Galilee.

He got into a boat with his disciples and . . . they put to sea, and as they sailed he fell asleep. When a squall came down on the lake the boat started taking in water and they found themselves in danger. So they went to rouse him saying, 'Master! Master! We are going down!' Then he woke up and rebuked the wind and the rough water; and they subsided and it was calm again. He said to them, 'Where is your faith?' They were awestruck and astonished and said to one another, 'Who can this be, that gives orders even to winds and waves and they obey him?'

(Luke 8:22–25)

To Read and Discuss
Look up other miracles in Matthew 9:18–34.
How many miracles did Jesus work in this passage?
Which is the most amazing or the most unusual?

To be able to control the forces of nature, to change death into life, to defeat evil and illness – all these great deeds were signs to the people that God's kingdom of peace, justice and freedom was starting to arrive. No wonder those who met him were amazed and began to realise that he was not just an ordinary man.

But it was only after Jesus had died and risen again that the apostles began to know and understand him more fully.

To Read and Write
You may remember how Jesus appeared to the apostles one evening when Thomas was not there and how this apostle refused to believe that Jesus was really alive. When he finally saw Jesus, what did Thomas say? (John 20).

....

....

So what do we as Catholics today believe about Jesus? The Gospels show clearly that Jesus:

A – was born of a virgin by the power of the Holy Spirit

B – had God's own powers of healing, forgiving sins and raising people to life and claimed that he was God's own Son

C – gave his Body and Blood at the Last Supper

D – died on the cross to save us from sin

E – rose from the dead.

These are all key Catholic beliefs about Jesus. Match the right letter next to the belief given below:

The Resurrection ....

The Virgin Birth ....

The Divinity of Christ ....

The Redemption ....

The Sacrifice of the Mass...........

For Discussion
Imagine how different everything would be if Jesus hadn't been God, but just a holy man.
What would have happened if he hadn't risen from the dead, but just died and stayed buried?
Why is the belief about the Virgin Birth important?

The Church Jesus founded, right from the time of the apostles, has always taught these things. We proclaim our faith in him as God and Man every Sunday at Mass when we say the Creed together:

I believe in one Lord, Jesus Christ, the Only Begotten Son of God, born of the Father before all ages. God from God, Light from Light, true God from true God, begotten, not made, consubstantial with the Father; through him all things were made.

For us men and for our salvation he came down from heaven, and by the Holy Spirit was incarnate of the Virgin Mary, and became man.

For our sake he was crucified under Pontius Pilate, he suffered death and was buried, and rose again on the third day in accordance with the Scriptures.

He ascended into heaven and is seated at the right hand of the Father.

He will come again in glory to judge the living and the dead, and his kingdom will have no end.

In the Creed, we call Jesus **'the Christ'** and of course his followers are called **Christians**. The word Christ is not his name; it is a word meaning 'the chosen one or anointed one of God'.
The Hebrew word that the Jewish people used was 'Messiah', but in the Greek language it becomes **Christos**.

To Write

What other words that we use contain this title 'Christ'?

....

....

Jesus tells us about himself

Let's now look at Jesus' own words about himself and what he means for us.
Many of his most important sayings are recorded in St John's Gospel.
Using a New Testament, look up these sayings, write them out below and then add your own words to show what you think they could mean.
(You might need to discuss this first.)

To Write

John 6:48

....

....

....

....

....

....

John 8:58

....

....

....

....

....

....

John 11:25

....

....

....

....

....

....

John 14:6

....

....

....

....

....

....

....

John 15:1

....

....

....

....

....

....

....

Jesus and me, his disciple

Remember what Thomas the apostle said when he saw the risen Jesus in the Upper Room? 'My Lord and My God!'

We believe that he is just that – God, become a man, so that he can really be one of us. Not a vision, or a ghost, or a pretence, but flesh and blood like us – though still divine. Son of Mary and Son of God.

As Christians – followers of Christ – we are called to rise up and follow him, just like the first disciples. Some of them had been great sinners; most were poor and may not even have been able to read and write. Some were afraid or reluctant at first.

To Think About
Can you remember the names of some of Jesus' followers who were sinners or outcasts before they met him?

We, like them, have to get to know him as a real person; we have to trust him and grow to love him like a friend. And we must give him our loyalty and follow him – even to the cross.

You might already know the simple prayer of a great English saint, Richard of Chichester:

May I know you more clearly
love you more dearly
and follow you more nearly.

As we prepare for Confirmation, this could become our prayer too.

In this Sacrament, Jesus the Son of God fills us with his love and with his Spirit, to strengthen our faith and to call us to serve him. Are we willing and ready to accept him?

For Discussion
What could a Catholic do to help a friend who did not know about Jesus Christ?
Why do you think Catholics often have a crucifix in their homes, or worn round their necks?

More Things to Read
The story of the death and resurrection of Jesus in one of the four gospels.

Parts of two of St Paul's letters: Philippians 2:5–11; Colossians 1:15–20

A poem by John Betjeman: *Christmas.*

Chapter 14 and 15 from *The Lion, the Witch and the Wardrobe* by C. S. Lewis about the death of Aslan.

Words to Know

Divine – *having the nature of God.*
Resurrection – *Jesus' rising from the dead.*
Redemption – *the saving or ransoming of someone from sin.*
Incarnation – *the joining of God and human flesh in Jesus.*
Apostle – *one of Jesus' chosen Twelve.*
Miracle – *an event which cannot be explained in an ordinary physical way; a wonder.*
Sacrifice – *something given up for the good of others.*

Session Two

Come,
O Holy Spirit

Heal our wounds, our strength renew;
On our dryness pour thy dew;
Wash the stain of guilt away.
Bend the stubborn heart and will;
Melt the frozen, warm the chill,
Guide the steps that go astray.

From a hymn to the Holy Spirit by
Stephen Langton (d. 1228)

VENI CREATOR SPIRITUS

Come, O Holy Spirit

In the short space of three years, Jesus gathered together a group of loyal followers – the disciples – and he taught them about himself and God his Father, about praying, about faith, about baptism and the Eucharist, about loving our neighbour, and the coming kingdom of God.

Then he was arrested and put to death: God's own Son suffering an agonising death, in public, on the cross. What were the disciples to think?

- That they had misunderstood his message?
- That he wasn't the Son of God after all?
- That everything in this life is a waste of time – even God loses?

After the Resurrection it was a different story. He told them that it was part of the plan; that only by going through with death could he, as God-made-Man, finally conquer it, and win eternal life for us all.

But what then? How was this message of hope and salvation to be given to everyone? Jesus' teaching was not to be for a small select band, but for everyone, and yet he said he was going back to the Father now.

This enormous task he left to twelve assorted men, not much in the eyes of the world, but hand-picked by Jesus to be his chosen apostles.

'Go, therefore, make disciples of all the nations; baptise them in the name of the Father and of the Son and of the Holy Spirit, and teach them to observe all the commands I gave you.'
(Matthew 28:19–20)

All nations! Even two thousand years ago that meant dozens of countries with different languages and religions. And Jesus wanted his living love and his teaching offered to every person in the world.

Let's look at what Jesus said to them during the last days before his death to prepare them for this great work.

In this passage from St Mark's Gospel, Jesus warns his followers that, because of the sinfulness of the world, their task will be dangerous and difficult. But they are not to fear:

'Be on your guard: they will hand you over to sanhedrins; you will be beaten in synagogues; and you will stand before kings and governors for my sake, to bear witness before them, since the Good News must first be proclaimed to all nations.

'And when they lead you away to hand you over, do not worry beforehand about what to say; no, say whatever is given to you when the time comes, because it is not you who will be speaking: it will be the Holy Spirit.'

(Mark 13:9–12)

And in St John's Gospel, Jesus says:

'The Advocate, the Holy Spirit whom the Father will send in my name will teach you everything and remind you of all I have said to you.'

(John 14:26)

Jesus promises that his own Spirit will be with them after he has gone to complete his own teaching and to stand by them when they need help. (An advocate is someone who stands by you or defends you, or speaks on your behalf.)

The Trinity

We Christians believe in **one** God. But he has revealed to us, through Jesus, a great mystery about himself: **he is Father, Son and Holy Spirit**, three persons but only one God. God is our Creator and Father, he is God's Son – our brother and saviour – and he is God's Holy Spirit, who comes down on us in Baptism and Confirmation, and lives in us all.
This great mystery about God's own life is called by Christians, the Trinity.

The coming of the Holy Spirit

Here is the account, from the Acts of the Apostles, of what happened when that promise of Jesus was fulfilled. This passage is always read in Mass on Pentecost Sunday.

When Pentecost day came round, they had all met together when suddenly there came from heaven a sound as of a violent wind, which filled the entire house in which they were sitting; and there appeared to them tongues as of fire; these separated and came to rest on the head of each of them. They were all filled with the Holy Spirit and began to speak different languages as the Spirit gave them power to express themselves.

Now there were devout men living in Jerusalem from every nation under heaven, and at this sound they all assembled, and each one was bewildered to hear these men speaking his own language ... 'Surely,' they said, 'all these men speaking are Galileans? How does it happen that each of us hears them in his own native language?' ... Everyone was amazed and perplexed; they asked one another what it all meant. Some, however, laughed it off. 'They have been drinking too much new wine,' they said. (Acts 2:1–8; 12–13)

For Discussion
What do you imagine the apostles felt like before this happened? Where were they? What were they doing?

What do you think happened to the apostles? How did the hearers react?

The coming of the Holy Spirit is described as 'a powerful wind' and 'tongues of fire'. What do these words tell us about the Spirit?

The apostles didn't keep their new strengths, gifts and powers to themselves. How are they still passed on in the Church today?

The gifts the Holy Spirit gives

The great prophet Isaiah, who lived seven centuries before Jesus Christ, wrote beautifully about what the Spirit brings to those people God chooses:

- **wisdom**
- **understanding**
- **knowledge**
- **counsel (the ability to give good advice)**
- **power (spiritual strength)**
- **holiness**
- **fear of the Lord.**

These are the gifts which are traditionally seen as coming to the Christian at Confirmation. These are the gifts and special strengths which we need to spread the message of Jesus, to

13

build up his Church, and to live in the world as good Catholics.

Confirmation is our own personal Pentecost. Like the apostles, we have a great task to do, and at Confirmation (which means literally 'being made firm') we are also changed like they were.

To Write
Think for a moment about each of these great gifts, and then write a sentence or two about each one, saying what you think it means:

wisdom ....

....

....

....

....

understanding ....

....

....

....

....

knowledge ....

....

....

....

....

counsel ....

....

....

....

....

power ....

....

....

....

....

holiness ....

....

....

....

....

fear of the Lord ....

....

....

....

....

For Discussion
Which gifts do you most lack?
How could a young Catholic use the gift of counsel?
Holiness is not just for the official, canonised saints. Have you ever met anyone you thought was holy?

The Lord, the Giver of life

The Holy Spirit, like Jesus, is someone real, a person we can know and love. He lives and acts in all God's people, moving us to pray and to worship, helping us to use our gifts and giving us God's own life to make us live.

It is much harder to think about the Holy Spirit than it is to think of Jesus, who is a human like us. The Holy Spirit of God hasn't got a body, or any other physical form: that's how he can live and work in all of us.
In the Creed, we state our faith in the Holy Spirit:

I believe in the Holy Spirit, the Lord, the giver of life, who proceeds from the Father and the Son, who with the Father and the Son is adored and glorified, who has spoken through the prophets.

The people of Israel before Jesus' time, the people of the Old Testament, knew that God made and loved and cared for them. They knew that his own Spirit lived in them, turning them to God and making them holy.

Their word for the Holy Spirit was **ruah** which means 'breath'. You may remember the story of the making of Adam in the Book of Genesis: God formed a man-shape out of clay or dust, and then breathed into it. This shows God giving his own spirit to human beings to make them really live. Without the Holy Spirit in our lives today, we would be dry and lifeless too.

Our response to God's gift of his Spirit

It would be a great mistake to think that when we receive the Holy Spirit at Confirmation we are automatically made perfect. God doesn't have a magic wand to wave over us to make us good and obedient – and even if he did, he wouldn't want to. We are his children, not his robots, and God wants our love and respect to be given freely.

It is all too easy to fall away from God, even when we mean well. It's even easier not to hear him when he tries to speak to us. It is our response to God which makes the difference – how we live our lives every day; whether we try to pray and to do his will.

Doing what God wants can be hard work – but the Holy Spirit will help us to do it. In a way, Confirmation is only the beginning: we must respond to the presence of the Holy Spirit who comes to us on our Confirmation day, and who will remain with us for the rest of our lives.

For Discussion
Would it be better if we were like robots instead of having 'free will'?
How can we know 'what God wants'?
When do you think it is most difficult to do what you know is right?

This is probably the most famous prayer to the Holy Spirit, which has been said by Christians for hundreds of years:

Come, Holy Spirit
Fill the hearts of your
faithful,
And kindle in them the
fire of your love.
Send forth your Spirit
And they shall be created
And you shall renew the
face of the earth.

You are likely to have some hymns to the Holy Spirit at your special Confirmation Mass. The first verse of one hymn by Bianco di Siena also makes a very good personal Confirmation prayer:

Come down O Love Divine
Seek thou this soul of mine
And visit it with thine own
Ardour glowing.
O Comforter draw near
Within my heart appear
And kindle it, thy holy
Flame bestowing.

For Discussion
'Young Catholics today need the gift of wisdom more than anything, especially in their social lives.' What do you think this might mean? Do you agree?

More Things to Read
From the Old Testament, Ezekiel's vision of dry bones – Chapter 37:1–14

St Paul's first letter to the Corinthians – Chapter 12:4–11.

Words to Know

Holy Spirit – God's own Spirit, sent to the apostles at Pentecost and coming to live in Christians especially in Baptism and Confirmation.

Trinity – the mystery of God being three persons, but still one God.

Apostle – one of Jesus' twelve specially chosen disciples who were the key figures in the early Church.

Pentecost – a great feast day of the Jewish people, fifty days after the Passover, now also a Christian feast when we remember the coming down of the Holy Spirit on the apostles.

Advocate – someone who speaks up for you, or defends you.

Free will – our human ability to make our own decisions, not just being 'programmed' by God.

Session Three

Members of Jesus' Church

You are a chosen race, a royal priesthood,
a holy nation, a people set apart.

From the first letter of St Peter

Members of Jesus' Church

One of the most important things about being confirmed is that it makes us full members of the Church which Jesus founded when he called together his apostles and sent them the Holy Spirit.

Sometimes we might think of 'the Church' as just a building or as a club. This would be quite wrong. The Church is the People of God, his own family.

God had a special family of chosen people even before Jesus came. These were the Israelites, and their story is told in the Old Testament.

The People of Israel

From the beginning of their history, God spoke to them about himself. One of the first people we hear about is Abraham. God promised him that he would have many descendants, making up a great nation, and that God would always be faithful and true to them.

God taught Israel through his great Law, given by Moses. He then gave them a land to settle in and a family of kings to rule them, and he spoke to them through the prophets.

For Discussion

What do you remember about Abraham?
Why did God make him this promise?
What are the most famous of the laws that God gave to Moses?
Do you know the names of any of the Old Testament prophets?
What is a prophet?
Why do you think that God called a whole people to hear his words and to be his own?

By doing all of this, he was getting his people ready for the time when he himself would come to teach, guide and speak to them – and to the whole world – when Jesus Christ was born nearly two thousand years ago.

One of the Eucharistic Prayers of the Mass – number four – sums up all this:

We give you praise, Father most holy, for you are great and you have fashioned all your works in wisdom and in love.
You formed man in your own image and entrusted the whole world to his care, so that in serving you alone, the Creator, he might have dominion over all creatures.
And when through disobedience he had lost your friendship, you did not abandon him to the domain of death.
For you came in mercy to the aid of all, so that those who seek might find you.
Time and again you offered them covenants and through the prophets taught them to look forward to salvation.
And you so loved the world, Father most holy, that in the fullness of time you sent your Only Begotten Son to be our Saviour.

This prayer sums up what we believe about the Old Testament – that through the people he had chosen and taught, God was getting the world ready for his own Son.

But what about after Jesus' ministry? Who or what would carry on his work when he had returned to his Father in heaven?

The Catholic Church carries on Jesus' work today

In our first and second sessions we learnt how Jesus then chose and taught his followers, passing on his work to them, and giving them his Holy Spirit to be with them always.

We know that after Jesus died, he rose again and lives for ever. And we know that he wanted his saving work to carry on when he had gone.

Let's look at some of the ways in which Jesus prepared his disciples, and what he said was to happen when he was no longer there.

You remember how Jesus asked his disciples who they thought he was. It was Simon, the fisherman, who answered up, 'You are the Christ, the Son of the Living God.'

In response to this profession of faith, Jesus told him he was to be called Peter – the Rock:

'You are Peter and on this rock I will build my church. And the gates of the underworld will never hold out against it. I will give you the keys of the kingdom

of heaven: whatever you bind on earth shall be considered bound in heaven; whatever you loose on earth shall be considered loosed in heaven.' (Matthew 16:18–19)

Peter was given this special mission by Jesus: the Church would depend on him and be guided by him. Under his leadership it would never fail but would remain true always.

Later, at the Last Supper, Jesus told the apostles that the bread and wine he gave them were his own Body and Blood, and that they should continue to:

'do this in memory of me.'

His Last Supper was the First Eucharist.

Just before he left them for the last time, he said they were to go to all nations and

'baptise them in the name of the Father and of the Son and of the Holy Spirit, and teach them to observe all the commands I gave you. And know that I am with you always; yes, to the end of time.'
(Matthew 20:19–20)

So Jesus lives in the Church he founded through –

- the teaching and guidance of the Pope and bishops – the successors of Peter and the apostles

- the sacraments – and especially the Eucharist, which is Jesus himself

- the living presence of his Holy Spirit

Look up the following passages in your Bible. In them we see the early Church carrying on Jesus' work:

To Write
The Church **baptises**: in the Acts of the Apostles, 2:38, St Peter says that everyone must

'...

....

....

....,'

The Church **celebrates the Eucharist**: in his First Letter to the Corinthians, 11:26, St Paul says

'...

....

....,'

23

The Church **teaches the truth**: in his First Lettter to Timothy, 6:3 St Paul warns of anyone who

'..

....

....

....,'

The Church is **a community**, the People of God: in the Acts of the Apostles, 2:42, we read that the new Christians

'..

....

....

....'

'One, holy, catholic and apostolic'

We say in the Creed at Mass:

'I believe in one, holy, catholic and apostolic Church.'

What do we mean when we say this?

We say that the Church is **one** because we all share the same faith and receive the same sacraments. We are especially united with each other when we receive the one Body and

Blood of Jesus Christ in the Eucharist.

These short passages are from St John's Gospel, chapter 17. Here Jesus is praying to the Father to keep his Church together in unity:

Father,
Keep those you have given me
True to your name,
So that they may be one like us
. . .

As you sent me into the world,
I have sent them into the world
. . .

May they all be one,
Just as, Father, you are in me and
I am in you.

The Church's founder was Jesus Christ, God made man, and so the Church is **holy**. It is through the Church that we meet the person of Jesus, even though he is not still on earth in a visible way, and through her too that we have the means to become holy – the sacraments.

If you look up the word **catholic** in a dictionary, you will see that it means 'universal'. So to call the Church 'catholic' means that Jesus founded it for all people in all places and at all times: it is not a national Church, and it is not tied to one particular culture.

Everyone, everywhere is called to be a member of the Church. The Catholic Church is for everyone.

Apostolic comes from the word apostle. Christ founded the Church on the twelve apostles who were then to take it 'to the ends of the earth'.

To Write
See how many of the original twelve apostles you can remember and write them below (look up St Mark's Gospel, 3:13–19 if you have forgotten any):

....

....

....

....

....

....

When the apostles died, others took their place. Soon those who were the new successors of the apostles began to be called **bishops**. We still have bishops to teach and rule the Church today under the leadership of

the Pope, the successor of Peter.

Our bishops are the apostles of today.

What is the Church like?

Jesus gave us two ideas of the Church to think about. He said it is like a **sheepfold**, with himself as the shepherd:

'I am the gate of the sheepfold ... Anyone who enters through me will be safe: such a one will go in and out and will find pasture.' (John 10:8–9)

He also described himself as a **vine**:

'I am the vine, you are the branches. Whoever remains in me with me in him, Bears fruit in plenty; for cut off from me you can do nothing.' (John 15:5)

St Paul, in writing to the Christians in Corinth, told them that they were **God's building**, his Temple and later that they were **Jesus' body** on earth:

'By the grace of God which was given me, I laid the foundations like a trained master-builder, and someone else is building on them. Now each one must be careful how he does the building . . .

(1 Corinthians 3:10)

'God has put all the separate parts into the body as he chose. If they were all the same part, how could it be a body? As it is, the parts are many but the body is one . . . Now Christ's body is yourselves, each of you with a part to play in the whole.'

(1 Corinthians 12:18–20, 27)

For Discussion
What does each of these four images help us to understand about the Church?

Whether we see ourselves as

• one of Jesus' sheep

• a branch of his vine

• part of his body, doing his work on earth or

• a stone in his house

our baptism has made each of us an important and much-loved part of the Church.

The Sacrament of Confirmation completes our Baptism, sealing and confirming us as God's own much-loved sons and daughters.

Here is a very old Christian prayer about the Church:

Think of your Church, O Lord.
Free it from all evil
And make it perfect in your love.
Make your people holy
And lead them to the kingdom you have prepared for them.
For yours is the power
And the glory
For all eternity.
Amen.

For Discussion
How would you answer someone who said: 'You can be a Christian on your own – there's no need to belong to a church'?

Words to Know

Apostolic – founded on the apostles or coming from the apostles.

Baptise – a sacrament or sacred action using water and words, which brings the Holy Spirit to the person and makes him or her a member of the Church, washing away sin.

Bishop – a successor of the apostles, teaching and ruling the Church right down to today.

Catholic – universal or world-wide, and including everything necessary.

Church – the community founded by Jesus Christ to continue his saving work.

Covenant – a promise or agreement.

Israelites – God's chosen people into which Jesus Christ his Son was born.

Old Testament – the holy writings of the Jewish people, telling the story of their relationship with God.

Saviour – someone who saves or brings help.

Meeting Jesus in the Sacraments

A sacramental celebration is a meeting of God's children with their Father, in Christ and the Holy Spirit; this meeting takes the form of a dialogue, through actions and words.

From the Catechism of the Catholic Church p. 1153

HOC·EST·ENIM·CORPVS·MEVM

Meeting Jesus in the Sacraments

In our first Session on Our Lord Jesus Christ we talked about how the Son of God was born into the human race, suffered and died and rose again. God was no longer going to be someone apart from us, distant and difficult to know. God, as we say in the Creed, 'was made Man'.

By doing this he could:

- show us the **way** to heaven himself

- teach us the **truth** from his own lips

- share with us his own divine **life**.

Do you remember that Jesus said

'I am the Way, the Truth and the Life'?

You'll find these words in St John's Gospel, chapter 14.

In the last session we saw that the Holy Spirit, working in the Church, carries on Jesus' work today, leading men along that **way** to God and teaching them the **truth**.

But how is Jesus' own **life** given to us today? The apostles and the other disciples, and the people Jesus cured, were able actually to be in his presence and to feel his love for them. How can we too meet him as a real person and receive his living love, his power and his grace, even though he no longer walks the earth?

Jesus gives us his life in the Sacraments

Today, through the Church he founded, Jesus carries on his life-giving work. He gives his grace – his saving help – to us at **special stages** in our lives, or for some **particular task** or role he wants us to do, or as part of our **daily needs**.

Through seven special actions called **sacraments**, the Church gives us Jesus' grace throughout our lives.

To Write

Here are the names of the seven sacraments of the Catholic Chuch. Match up the words with the right sentences.

Confirmation   Penance

Baptism

The Anointing of the Sick

Ordination

Matrimony   The Eucharist

....i s the name of the sacrament which a baby or a new Christian receives to make him or her part of Jesus' Church, filled with the Holy Spirit. It cleanses the person's soul from Original Sin and gives them a share in God's life.

.... is the sacrament when the Holy Spirit comes down on us as he did on the apostles to make us ready for being a Christian in the world. It completes what began at baptism.

.... means 'thanksgiving' – we offer bread and wine to God and it becomes Jesus' Body and Blood. When we receive this sacrament, Jesus feeds us and we become one with him and with each other.

.... t a k e s place when a man whom God has specially called, becomes a priest.

.... j o i n s two people together for life by their vows. They are given the graces they need to grow in love of God and each other, and to create a family.

.... is the sacrament in which God's forgiveness fills our hearts if we repent of our sins to a priest and do an act of penance to help put things right again with God and our neighbour. We are reconciled to God.

.... strengthens the very ill and the dying.

Jesus acts in our lives today through these seven Sacraments. He comes to us and gives us special graces for all the important needs and events of our lives, from birth to death. Through the seven Sacraments he marks us out as his own.

We could say that through the Sacraments:

'we come to share in the divinity of Christ, who humbled himself to share in our humanity.'

For Discussion
When do we hear these words? Can you explain what they mean?

Outward signs – inward reality

Because Jesus lived a human life like ours, he knows that we need help to believe in him and to understand what he does. And so he comes to us in ways that we can really **feel, see or hear** – we don't need some special knowledge or sixth sense: the five we have already will do.

Each of these sacraments, in which Jesus comes to us through the actions of the Church, has an **outward sign** attached to it so that we can see and understand what God is doing.

For Discussion
Think of some signs that we all come across every day – not only ones you can see (like a heart on a Valentine card) but also ones you can hear (like a siren on an ambulance).
Which ones are especially good at telling us what is going on, or what we have to do?

Each Sacrament has its own outward sign which shows us what Jesus is doing.

It might be an action (such as the pouring of water in baptism) or a form of words (such as the exchange of vows in marriage) or both.

Unlike the signs we thought about just now, these sacramental signs actually achieve something – when the sign is performed, God acts on us in the Sacrament.

Let's look at each of the Sacraments in turn and see how Jesus enters our lives and makes us holy in each of them.

Baptism

In Baptism the outward sign used is

....

What does this show is happening in this Sacrament?
What does the priest say as he does it?
Have you been to a baptism recently? What other signs and symbols are used?

....

....

....

....

In **Penance** (sometimes called the Sacrament of Reconciliation or Confession) God forgives us our sins; we are reconciled to him and to his family, the Church; we are given strength to stay close to him and to resist sin in the future.

What do *we* have to do it we are to be forgiven by God in this sacrament?

....

....

....

....

....

The **Eucharist** is the heart of the Church and the greatest of the sacraments. It is Jesus Christ himself really present among us today to fill us with his own life – his Body and Blood. We receive the Eucharist in the Mass, which is a renewal of Jesus' sacrifice on Calvary.

The outward signs of this great sacrament are ....

....

....

....

and the words said by the priest, which Jesus himself said at the Last Supper (Luke 22:19–20).

....

....

....

....

....

What do the signs of bread and wine tell us about the Eucharist?

VENI CREATOR SPIRITUS

In **Confirmation** Jesus gives his Holy Spirit to each of us as he did to the apostles at Pentecost; we become 'temples' of the Holy Spirit; we are taken more deeply into the life of Jesus; we receive great gifts and strengths to serve Jesus as apostles.

Look at the second letter of St Paul to the Corinthians, chapter 1 verses 21–22. St Paul says:

'It is God himself ....

....

....

....

....

....

....'

This shows us what Confirmation is about. There will of course be much more about Confirmation in a later session.

Marriage joins a man and a woman in the name of Christ, and makes them a sign of his never-ending love for mankind. They have and bring up sons and daughters for God; they receive the strength to be faithful to God and each other, and to keep the vows they made on their wedding day. Do you know what the vows say?

....

....

....

....

....

....

....

....

....

Ordination makes a man a priest for ever; he offers his whole life to God. He receives through this sacrament the powers and responsibilities which Jesus first gave to the apostles; he takes on the role of Jesus, sharing his priesthood.

In what ways does a priest take the part of Jesus in the life of the Church today?

....

....

....

....

The Anointing of the Sick brings Jesus' help and strength to those who are ill or dying; they meet Jesus himself in this sacrament and he – through the priest – lays on them his healing hand. These stories from the Gospels show Jesus doing the same thing 2000 years ago:

- The two blind men – Matthew 9:27–31
- The leper – Mark 1:40–45
- The man born blind – John 9:1–7.

Look up one of these and choose someone to read it aloud to the group.

The sacraments in our lives

Each of us has received the sacrament of Baptism which made us a son or daughter of God, and which gave us new life in Christ. You are now getting ready to receive the sacrament of Confirmation from the hands of the bishop. This will make you a full member of Jesus' Church – completing what your Baptism began – and will bring the Holy Spirit to live in you.

Here is a prayer adapted from part of the famous 'Jesus Psalter'. You could use it as you approach your Confirmation day:

Jesus, strengthen me
in body and soul.
Make me want to
change my life,
to make up for the
wrong things in my past:
thoughts, words, deeds and
habits.
Make my heart obedient to you,
ready to do all things for you.
By your Holy Spirit help me
to live a virtuous life.
And let all the holy sacraments
I receive,
bring me to your
heavenly kingdom.
Amen.

For Discussion
When we were baptised, our Godparents made promises on our behalf. What kind of things should become our own responsibilities when we are older? How could a young Catholic show that the Mass is important to them?

Words to Know

Sign – *something you can see or hear, smell, touch or taste which points or directs you to something else, like a sign-post or a warning light.*

Sacrament – *a grace-giving action of God in our lives, in which an outward sign shows us what is happening, and also brings it about.*

Eucharist – *the offering, in thanksgiving, of bread and wine, which become the Body and Blood of Jesus Christ at the consecration in the Mass.*

Anointing – *strengthening or healing someone or setting them apart for a special task. Jesus' title 'Christ' means 'anointed'.*

Ordination – *the sacrament in which a man becomes a priest.*

More to Read
'Where Love Is, God Is' – a short story by the Russian writer, Leo Tolstoy.

Session Five

Living the Life of an Apostle

Stay with me, and then I shall begin to shine as you shine, so to shine as to be a light to others.
Make me preach you without preaching – not by words, but by my example.

Cardinal John Henry Newman

SCT·THOMA·&·IOANNES
ORATE·PRO·NOBIS

Living the Life of an Apostle

In the last session we talked about how we meet Jesus really and personally in the sacraments. The sacraments are some of the most important ways in which we grow towards to be more like Jesus Christ.

We saw how the sacrament of Confirmation

- makes us full members of Jesus' Church
- completes our Baptism
- gives us the strengths and gifts of God's Holy Spirit and
- makes us grow in our own spiritual lives.

These are all the things God does for us in Confirmation. But we have a part to play too.

The apostles received the Holy Spirit at Pentecost: what did they do then? Did they sit around in Jerusalem feeling holy, or boast of their new gifts? Did they shrug their shoulders and say 'Thanks God, but what happens now?' Of course not – they went out as Jesus had told them to and began to teach and baptise the world.

In a way, Confirmation is our own personal Pentecost. It is a great gift from God, and it is also a special call to be his witnesses in the world. It is the beginning of our life as an apostle.

Once we are confirmed, we must start to act as full members of the Church – to be **active** Catholics.

How can we be witnesses for Jesus?

Like the apostles, we are obliged to work for Jesus Christ, to spread his good news and to grow to be like him.

There are a number of important ways in which a confirmed Catholic can do this.

To Write
(Fill in the blanks if you can.)

We can

1. keep close to him by going to .... and receiving him in Communion

2. receive his loving forgiveness in the Sacrament of Penance or ....

3. keep in touch with him whenever we can by.............

4. live a life worthy of one of his ....

5. bring others to him by .... our faith

6. put others .... and help them for his sake

Let's look at each of these in turn.

1. Sunday Mass

One thing that most people know about Catholics is that they have to go to Church on Sundays, but why do we have to? Isn't it better to just go, or not, as it suits you – perhaps not at all, perhaps on another day?

The Church says that all Catholics must go to Mass every Sunday and Holyday – unless there is some serious problem which prevents us. This tradition goes right back to the beginnings of Christianity.

We know from the Old Testament that the Jewish people worshipped on every Sabbath day, as the third commandment required. And we know from the gospels that Jesus himself was no exception. He and his disciples carried on 'keeping the Sabbath holy' by going to the synagogue. That was on the seventh day of their week – Saturday.

But after Jesus rose from the dead on 'the first day of the week', that day, **Sunday**, became the new holy day for Christians. We can read in the Acts of the Apostles and in the letters of St Paul that right from the earliest days, the Sunday Mass has been the centre of life and worship for the followers of Christ.

Look up in the Acts of the Apostles chapter 2 verse 42, and chapter 20 verse 7: what did they call the Mass then?

....

For Catholics today too going to Mass means sharing in the great mystery of Jesus really present in the Eucharist. In the Mass, we remember Jesus dying and rising and bringing us new life through the sacrifice of his own life on the cross. This is why we call the Mass a sacrifice. But it is more than just a 'remembering'; it is also a real sharing in that Sacrifice, made present on the altar again by the words and actions of the priest.

When we are at Mass, we are there at the Last Supper, and at the foot of the cross, with the apostles.

Like the apostles, we are not on our own. We make up the Church. We belong to each other because we each belong to Christ and we make up his Body in the world. The Sunday Mass is the heart of our Catholic life where we meet Jesus in Communion and worship together as fellow disciples. It isn't the same just saying a quick prayer on your own at any old time of the week.

To Discuss and Write
What would you say are the most important parts of the Mass?
What are the Holydays and how many can you remember?

List as many as you can:

....

....

....

....

....

2. The Sacrament of Penance

The other important way in which we meet Christ frequently, is to go to him in the sacrament of Penance to ask for his forgiveness of our sins and for his healing love.

We can read in the gospels about Jesus forgiving the sins of those who came to him and repented. Look up the story of the woman who was a sinner in Luke 7:36–50.

Jesus still forgives sins today through the sacrament of Penance. He passed on his power to forgive to the apostles when he said to them:

'Receive the Holy Spirit.
For those whose sins you forgive,
they are forgiven;
for those whose sins you
retain, they are retained.'
(John 20:22–23)

Catholic priests have this power today to grant Jesus' forgiveness to those who are sorry and make a good confession.

The Church asks Catholics to go to the Sacrament of Confession at least once every year – as a minimum. This should always include receiving the Sacrament during Lent or soon after Easter.

> **For Discussion**
> *What do you think would be a 'good confession'?*
> *What might make a confession 'bad'?*
> *Why do you think the Church obliges Catholics to go yearly at least?*
> *Why should this be near Easter?*

3. Prayer

There is really only one way to find out about prayer – and that is to pray!

It has been called 'the raising of the mind and heart to God' or 'speaking to God' or 'listening to God'. It is the way in which we remain in touch with him; we direct our thoughts to him; we try to live in his presence, just as we might think constantly about some person we love who is away. That is what it should be like with God.

There are many sides to prayer:

- praising and adoring God
- thanking him
- asking forgiveness
- asking for particular things
- trying to find out what God wants of us getting to know him better
- just thinking about him.

> **For Discussion**
> *Which of these is the easiest to do?*
> *Or the most difficult?*
> *Think about the Our Father, the prayer Jesus taught the disciples: which aspects of prayer are found in it?*

We also pray to Our Lady and the saints, though not in the same way. We don't worship them and ask for their forgiveness – this is for God only. But we can ask them for help and encouragement, or sometimes for particular things. After all, we do this to those who love and care for us here on earth – we can ask those who are with God in heaven in just the same way.

To Write

Try to think of any saints that you have heard of who are 'patron saints' of particular things or places, for example: St Andrew is the patron saint of Scotland.

....

....

....

....

....

Write here the saint you have chosen to be your own Confirmation patron:

....

4. To live a life worthy of Jesus

'You must be perfect, just as your heavenly Father is perfect.'

Jesus makes this great demand on us. It sounds impossible. But he gives us the way to follow: we must model ourselves on him. Whatever we are doing or deciding, we should ask ourselves:

- what did he do?
- what did he say?
- what would he do or say if he were here now?
- what were his standards?

- what does his Church say about it?

To Read and Write

We could look first of all at Jesus' own summary of what is good, in the Beatitudes (Matthew 5:1–12).

What do you think he meant by 'poor in spirit' and 'pure in heart'?

....

....

....

Now read St Paul's letter to the Ephesians, 4:25–5:9. What is he warning them against?

....

....

....

What are the good qualities which are the opposite of these faults?

....

....

....

St Paul summed up how Christians should live in the world by saying:

'This may be a wicked age, but your lives must redeem it'.

The same is true today.

45

5. As apostles, we must spread the faith

When we are confirmed we become apostles of Christ in the world.

This means that we now have to get to know and love our faith more and to teach it to others. We can support others in their faith. We have to be like the apostle Andrew who brought his brother Simon to meet Jesus, or like Philip who brought his friend Bartholomew. (You can read about them in chapter 1 of St John's gospel).

The Church tells us that we do this: 'by word and by deed' and that 'the young should become the first apostles of the young'. No-one else could do it so well.

> **For Discussion**
> *How best could a young Catholic be a 'good advertisement' for their faith?*
> *What difficulties might they meet in trying to practise their faith today?*

6. To serve others for Jesus' sake

One important aspect of being a disciple of Jesus, is that we should follow his example of **service**. This means more than vaguely 'being nice to people' or 'keeping out of trouble'. It means putting others first and yourself last all the time.

It might mean being unselfish with your time, attention, friendship and money; perhaps trying to care about those you don't like, as well as those you do like.

To Read and Write
What did Jesus say about our treatment of others? Look up each of these sayings of Jesus from the Gospels and write down the main message of each:

Luke 6:27–29:

....

....

....

Mark 10:41–45:

....

....

....

John 15:12–13:

....

....

Here is a prayer which was written by St. Ignatius of Loyola in the 16th century. See if you can learn it before your Confirmation:

Lord, teach me to serve you as you deserve;
to give,
and not to count the cost;
to fight,
and not to heed the wounds;
to toil,
and not to seek for rest;
to labour,
and to ask for no reward,
except that of knowing
that I do your will.

To Read
The story of Father Damien of Molokai – a great example of a saint who served others and who knew the importance of faith, prayer and the Sacraments. There are various versions – long and short – of his life's story.

Session Six

Confirmation: The Rite

Give them the spirit of wisdom and understanding, the spirit of right judgment and courage, the spirit of knowledge and reverence.
Fill them with the spirit of wonder and awe in your presence.

From the Bishop's prayer to the Holy Spirit in the Confirmation rite.

ALLELVIA

Confirmation: The Rite

No-one can ever be completely ready to receive Jesus' promised Spirit in Confirmation, or can ever be worthy of it. But the Sacraments are about *what Jesus does for us* – the ways in which he enters our lives and makes them holy. As long as we *want* to meet him in the Sacrament of Confirmation, that is enough for him.

With only a short time to go until Confirmation, this session goes through what happens on the day.

To help you really know what is going on, we will see:

- what the ceremony is like
- what signs and symbols will be used
- what will be said and done
- who will be there.

What is the Confirmation ceremony like?

The Sacrament of Confirmation will be given to you (we usually say 'conferred on you') by the Bishop at a special Confirmation Mass. The actual Confirmation will take place between the Gospel and the Offertory.

Let's just remind ourselves of the order of events in the Mass, and see where Confirmation itself will fit in.

Here are the main parts of the Mass in a jumbled up order. See if you can sort them out:

Sermon   **Gospel**
          Going to Communion
          Offertory
Bidding prayers
          Old Testament Reading
          Consecration
                    Blessing
New Testament Reading
                    Creed
     Psalm   **The 'I confess'**

To Write
Correct order:

....

....

....

51

....

....

....

....

....

....

....

....

....

Your Confirmation will take place after the Gospel.

There are four important parts to the Confirmation itself:

First, the priest will **present** all the Confirmation candidates (as you are called) to the Bishop. The Bishop then talks to you all in his **Sermon**.

After this you say again the promises that were made on your behalf at Baptism. This is called the **renewal of baptismal promises**.

Then comes the very important **laying on of hands** by the Bishop over all the candidates together.

Each candidate then goes forward one at a time to receive **the anointing with chrism** by the Bishop.

And after every candidate has been anointed, the Mass carries on as normal with the Bidding Prayers, the Offertory and so on.

There is a special blessing at the end for all those newly confirmed.

The conferring of the Sacrament

Let's look more closely at the three most important parts of the Confirmation rite in which the Sacrament will be given to you.

The Renewal of Baptismal Promises

As we have seen, the Sacrament of Baptism is the beginning of our life in Jesus Christ and makes us members of his Church, freeing us from the grip of sin. Most of us will have been baptised as babies and so will remember nothing about it. If you have been to a Baptism recently, you will know that the parents and Godparents of the child, who present him or her to the Church to become a son or daughter of God, have to make promises rejecting evil and accepting the faith of the Church.

Now, in Confirmation, you will make them again for yourself. This Sacrament will complete your Baptism, taking you fully into Jesus' life and love, and sealing you with his Spirit as a full member of his Church. So you should be ready to renew these vows for yourself now, and you should mean to live up to them.

The Bishop will ask you all some questions. You will renew your baptismal promises by replying

'I do.'

The first question is:

'Do you renounce Satan, and all his works and empty promises?'

For Discussion
What do you think is meant by 'his works' and his 'empty promises'?
When in the Gospels did Jesus refuse to give in to the Devil?

The rest of the questions sum up the Creed, and by answering them you will be proclaiming your faith in God the Father, Jesus Christ his son, the Holy Spirit and the Catholic Church, just as you do every Sunday. Each time, you answer 'I do'.

The Bishop will finish this part by saying:

**'This is our faith.
This is the faith of the Church.
We are proud to profess it
in Christ Jesus our Lord.'**

And everyone will reply 'Amen'.

The laying on of hands over all the candidates

The Bishop will stretch out his hands over the heads of all the candidates for Confirmation, as he prays that God will send his Holy Spirit 'to confirm them with his abundant gifts, and through his anointing conform them more fully to Christ the Son of God.' Usually you will stay in your places for this.

The anointing with the oil of chrism

Then comes the actual giving

of the Sacrament to each individual.

The Bishop will place his hand on the head of each person, and making the sign of the cross on the forehead with **chrism**.

This 'laying on of hands' is a very ancient symbol. In Old Testament times, it meant:

- a blessing flowing from one person to another
- passing on power and authority
- giving God's spirit for a special purpose.

When, after Pentecost, the apostles passed on the gift of the Holy Spirit to their new converts, they used the same gesture – the laying on of hands – to show what they were doing.

To Read and Write
Look up in the Acts of the Apostles 8:14–17 and write out here the key part of the passage:

Peter and John prayed

....

....

....

....

....

This gesture is still used today in Confirmation. It shows how the Holy Spirit comes down and lives in those who are Confirmed, even though we cannot see him. The Bishop does today what the apostles first did nearly 2000 years ago.

> **To Think About**
> *Usually a **Bishop** confirms. What is a bishop and why does he usually do Confirmations?*

Remember that every Bishop is a **successor of the apostles** of Christ, who themselves received the Holy Spirit at Pentecost. The role and the powers of the apostles has been handed down through the centuries, through all the Catholic Bishops in history, to our Bishops today. They pass on the great gifts that God gives us in the Church.

The **chrism** which is used to anoint the forehead with the sign of the cross is also full of meaning. It is a perfumed oil made of olive oil and balsam, which is blessed by the Bishop on Maundy Thursday. It is a powerful and ancient symbol of healing and the giving of strength.

The word 'chrism', as you might have guessed, comes from the same word as 'Christ'. It is really a Greek word: *chrio* means 'anoint'. Jesus Christ is 'the anointed one' of God.

Chrism makes us too the anointed ones of God – the specially chosen – for we share in Jesus' own life through this sacrament.

When the Bishop lays his hand on your forehead on Confirmation day, and signs you with chrism, he says the words:

> 'N. (your name), be sealed with the Gift of the Holy Spirit.'

You reply: 'Amen.'

That is the moment at which you are confirmed. The laying on of hands, the anointing with chrism and the Bishop's words, are the 'outward sign' of the sacrament.

For Discussion

When the Bishop says 'be sealed with the gift of the Holy Spirit', what does the word 'sealed' mean? Why do important documents have seals on them? How does this apply to us once we are confirmed?

To Read

Look up again (we read it in Session Four) what St Paul says to the Corinthian Christians in his second letter to them, 1:21–22.

Most churches will have a practice for the Confirmation mass, so that everyone knows what to expect and where they should be. Make sure that you know when yours is going to be.

Once you are Confirmed

After Confirmation day is over, you will have to start thinking about some big questions that being a confirmed Catholic brings up:

'Confirmation was my Pentecost: how can I be an apostle for Christ in the world? At school? At home? In my social life?'

'Now I am confirmed, I must take responsibility for my own personal religious life: how can I learn more about my faith? How can I become better at praying? How often should I go to Confession?'

'Confirmation has made me a full member of Jesus' Church:

how can I play my part? Can I join something in the parish? Can I help with money-raising for good causes? Are there any people in my parish or my school, my town or my village who need my help?'

'What kind of person does God want me to be?'

These are questions for you to answer as you grow in knowledge and understanding of what it means to be a Catholic.

Here is a final prayer at the end of this course, which asks God to help us to be what he wants, so that we, like Jesus Christ, can bring God's love into the world. It is usually called 'The Prayer of St Francis'.

Lord,
Make me an instrument of
your peace;

where there is hatred let me
sow love;
where there is injury let me
sow pardon;
where there is doubt let me
sow faith;
where there is despair let me
give hope;
where there is darkness let me
give light;
where there is sadness let me
give joy.

O divine master, grant that I
may not try to be comforted,
but to comfort,
not try to be understood, but
to understand,
not try to be loved, but to
love.

Because it is in giving that we
receive,
it is in forgiving that we are
forgiven;
and it is in dying that we are
born to eternal life.